INSTANT ART
for
BIBLE WORKSHEETS

Book Four

Compiled by
Eleanor Sayers
Michael Forster

Drawn by
Arthur Baker

Kevin
Mayhew

First published in 1994 in Great Britain by
KEVIN MAYHEW LTD
Rattlesden
Bury St Edmunds, Suffolk IP30 0SZ

ISBN 0 86209 515 8
Catalogue No 1396024

Cover design by Roy Mitchell
Typesetting and page creation by Anne Haskell
   assisted by Vicky Brown
Printed in Great Britain

Introduction

Following the success of Books 1, 2 and 3 in the *Instant Art for Bible Worksheets* series, we are delighted to offer a fourth collection.

As before, these sheets are intended to be a resource for a variety of applications: family services, Sunday schools, mid-week clubs, holiday clubs and for use in day schools. They have been designed so that children of varying ages and abilities can use them at their own level.

The sheets are designed to be used in conjunction with, and not in place of, an accompanying talk.

• day school use
The worksheets lend themselves to follow-up work from a school or class assembly or a class lesson, for which they can be adapted, if necessary.

For the infant age group, the word search puzzles could either be deleted altogether or replaced by a simple word exercise. For the junior age group, the picture could be replaced by comprehension questions, multi-choice answer questions or similar exercises.

• photocopy/cut out
Unlike some of the titles in the 'Instant Art' series, this book has been compiled as a collection of single page worksheets, the assumption being that users will reproduce a particular page (as a unit) in the quantities they require. However, individual items could be combined with other material and used in whatever way is most helpful. Our aim continues to be to provide material that is versatile and flexible in use.

As before, the pages have been printed on one side only to give the best possible quality of reproduction from a photocopier. The book's format allows it to be placed flat on the photocopier.

• Bible editions
We have used the *New International Version* or the *Good News Bible*, the two editions which our research shows are the most commonly used by children.

• contents
A list of worksheets contained in this collection, together with scriptural references and page numbers, is given overleaf.

• copyright
Material in this book is copyright-free provided that it is used for the purpose for which the book is intended. The usual copyright restrictions apply to any use for *commercial* purposes.

Users' Responses
Sales of books in the Palm Tree Press 'Instant Art' series continue to prove that they are meeting a need. The series is now developing in response to, and with the help of, people who have found material in the existing books useful. *Your* ideas or suggestions for new titles would be warmly received and carefully considered!

Contents

Read Genesis 2:15-end

Can you name the plants and animals?

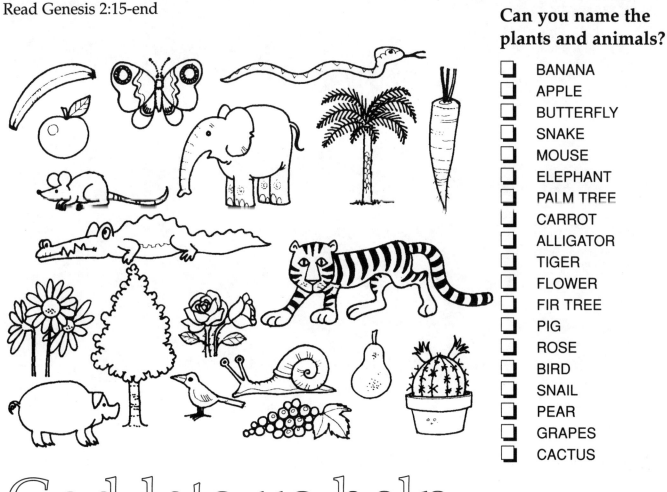

- ❏ BANANA
- ❏ APPLE
- ❏ BUTTERFLY
- ❏ SNAKE
- ❏ MOUSE
- ❏ ELEPHANT
- ❏ PALM TREE
- ❏ CARROT
- ❏ ALLIGATOR
- ❏ TIGER
- ❏ FLOWER
- ❏ FIR TREE
- ❏ PIG
- ❏ ROSE
- ❏ BIRD
- ❏ SNAIL
- ❏ PEAR
- ❏ GRAPES
- ❏ CACTUS

God lets us help

**The garden is rather dull – can you brighten
it up with some flowers and trees?**

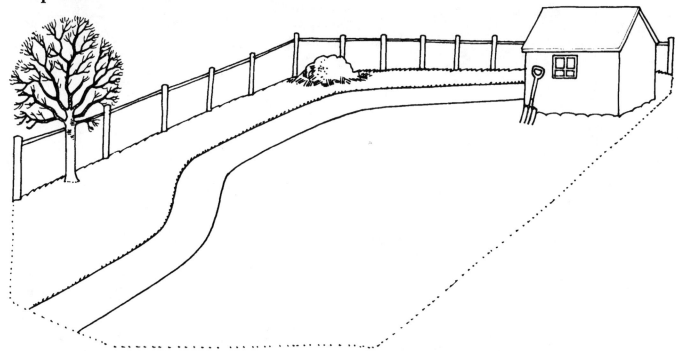

A riddle:
Why did God make the woman?

Answer:
Because after he had made the man, he
thought, 'I must be able to do better!'

Read Genesis 3

Find the snake and colour the picture

Everyone says, 'It's not my fault!'

Crack the code

T H B E N S O

Spot the 9 Differences

God called Abram

From _____ (Gen 11:31) **to** _____ (Gen 12:5)

From   The present   **to**   The future

Forward to the future

Jesus calls us to move

From

Word search

F	A	L	S	E	H	O	O	D	K
L	S	O	R	O	D	N	C	E	P
B	R	A	J	E	V	F	T	A	C
H	K	S	H	R	E	A	Q	T	U
X	N	D	E	A	H	R	Z	H	Q
R	I	A	P	S	E	D	E	A	M
T	A	J	G	W	Y	P	F	T	F
V	G	W	D	S	R	U	M	X	A
I	Y	X	T	P	A	F	E	A	S
D	E	S	P	O	E	B	L	H	G
W	I	C	A	Z	F	D	A	L	B

FEAR   HATE   DESPAIR
FALSEHOOD   WAR   DEATH

To

T	R	U	T	H	G	M	U	Y	F
S	N	Z	D	Q	O	A	W	O	X
U	H	V	L	I	Z	P	E	A	C
R	P	B	L	R	X	C	E	C	N
T	R	U	S	P	E	F	A	T	Y
J	E	F	K	R	I	K	U	E	P
T	C	H	J	L	O	V	X	Q	I
I	W	E	Q	F	B	K	M	O	G
L	R	V	D	V	E	C	A	E	P
O	H	O	P	N	H	N	J	S	M
N	B	L	I	F	R	D	G	A	S

TRUTH   HOPE   TRUST
LIFE   PEACE   LOVE

**Join the dots to find
a symbol of peace**

**Can you fill in the missing words
to complete the prayer?**

Lead me from DEATH to _ _ _ _
          from FALSEHOOD to _ _ _ _ _
Lead me from DESPAIR to _ _ _ _
          from FEAR to _ _ _ _ _
Lead me from HATE to _ _ _ _
          from WAR to _ _ _ _ _

Jacob shows his bravery

Read Genesis 33

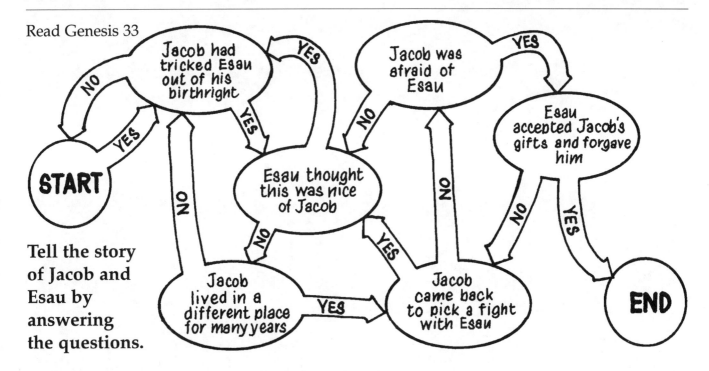

Tell the story of Jacob and Esau by answering the questions.

What God wants isn't always the easiest thing to do.
Draw a circle round the thing that would have been easier for Jacob to do.
Draw a square round the thing that God wanted him to do.

TO KEEP AWAY FROM
ESAU FOR EVER

TO TRY AND MAKE UP
WITH ESAU

Put the first letter of the picture in each box to show what Esau did.

Read Exodus 12:37-39

Here are the people leaving Egypt.
Can you find their animals?

Journey to freedom

Plan your escape. **What would you wear?**

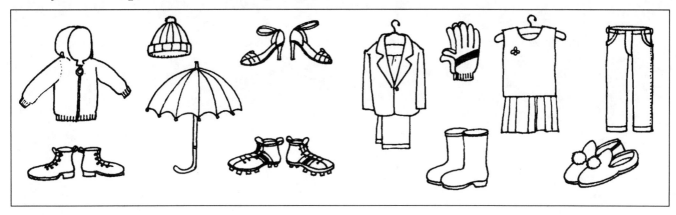

You've got to move fast! **What food would you take?**

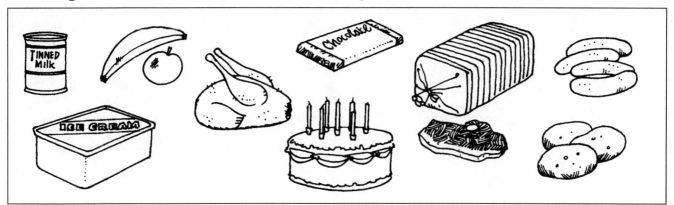

Read Exodus 17:8-16

While the Israelites were camping in the desert, some people called the Amalekites came and attacked them.

JOSHUA

Moses put Joshua in charge of getting the Israelite army together.

Moses held up the staff as a sign that he was appealing to God for help.

While his arms were up, the _____ were winning, but when he put his arms down, the _____ started to win.

Moses stood on top of the hill, holding the staff of God in his hands. But soon his arms got tired.

Look up Exodus 17:12
How did Moses keep his arms in the air?
Draw a picture here.

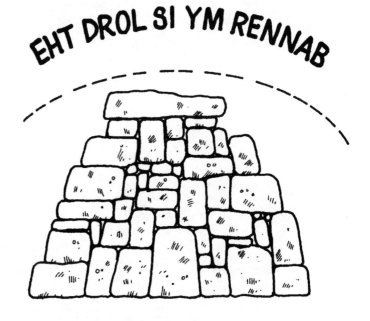

EHT DROL SI YM RENNAB

Moses built an altar to say 'thank you' to God. **Spell the words backwards to see what he called it.**

Read Exodus 35

God is on the move

Word search

What would you need to make a tent?

D	G	O	E	C	F	A	O	B	D
V	B	H	D	A	E	R	H	T	P
K	E	J	V	N	N	Q	N	U	N
A	M	U	M	V	I	A	G	E	Z
W	S	E	S	A	L	C	E	H	S
L	E	B	A	S	Y	D	P	F	E
C	L	M	G	S	L	T	A	R	P
T	O	E	X	E	U	D	T	I	O
W	P	G	S	P	S	R	F	Y	R
C	Q	K	Z	J	H	X	E	R	E

POLES

PEGS

CANVAS

ROPES

NEEDLES

THREAD

TAPE

MEASURE

Change the words in bold to others which rhyme with them, to correct the sentences.

Moses was told to build a **vent** for God (v 11)

People gave their **mould** to Moses (v 5)

Fed bull was used for decoration (v 25)

They also used the skin of **clams** (v 23)

Other people gave fine **weather** (v 23)

A lot of work was done by **savers**, **diners** and **beavers** (v 35)

Could you design a tent for God?

Read Judges 4

THE CHARACTERS
Join up the names to the descriptions.
(One has been done for you already)

DEBORAH	The person chosen to be in charge of Israel's army
BARAK	Jael's husband and ally of Jabin
SISERA	Prophetess in charge of Israel
HEBER THE KENITE	Commander of Jabin's (Israel's enemy's) army
JAEL	She tricked Sisera into coming into her tent and killed him while he was asleep.

Sisera was the only one of Jabin's army to escape. **Which route takes him to Jael's tent?**

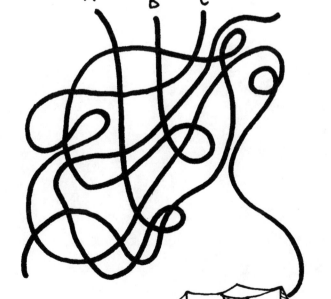

A bit of a gory story. **But what does it tell us?** (Crack the code to find out)

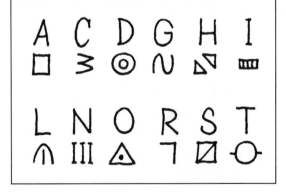

A	C	D	G	H	I
□	⋛	◉	∿	⊿	▥

L	N	O	R	S	T
⋀	III	△	⅂	⊠	⊙

⊙⊿⅂□⊙ ∿△◉ ▥⊠

‾ ‾ ‾ ‾ ‾ ‾ ‾ ‾ ‾ ‾ ‾

▥ III ⋛△III⊙⅂△⋀

‾ ‾ ‾ ‾ ‾ ‾ ‾ ‾ ‾

Read 1 Samuel 17:1-51

Biggest isn't always best

Colour the best in each pair

Get the bus to the depot

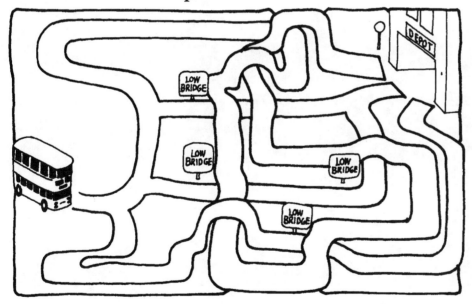

Crack the code

A B E F G I L M N S T U W Y

GODDEN OF TANGATE BEST

OF IT EVER KNOWS

NOT BY SWORD OR SPEAR

Saul anointed king

Read 1 Samuel 9

Saul is looking for his father's five donkeys.
Can you see them?

God wanted Saul to be anointed King by Samuel, who was a prophet.
Why did Saul and his servants go to see Samuel?
(Look up 1 Samuel 9:5-6) _____

_____

**Fit these words from the story
into the right spaces:**

<u>4 Letters</u>
SAUL
KING

<u>7 Letters</u>
PROPHET
SERVANT

<u>6 Letters</u>
ANOINT
SAMUEL
DONKEY

<u>8 Letters</u>
BENJAMIN

Samuel was told by God that someone from the tribe of Benjamin would come to see him the next day, and that he was to anoint him as King. When Saul arrived, Samuel knew that he was the right person.

Read 1 Kings 1

Solomon has been anointed, but he hasn't a crown:
can you find him one in the picture?

Find a rhyming word for the one in bold, to correct the sentences:
(Verse numbers refer to the Good New Bible)

Solomon rode to Gihon on a **fool** (v 44)

Zadok was a **beast** (v 26) and Nathan was a **soffit** (v 23)

They celebrated with noisy **crumpets** (v 39)

The ground shook because of all the **boys** (v 39)

They hoped that Solomon's reign would be even more **preposterous** than David's (v 40)

Word search

C	N	O	M	O	L	O	S	M	G
N	T	H	N	G	A	S	C	A	M
N	B	A	T	H	S	H	E	B	A
A	E	I	I	R	D	H	O	I	V
H	N	B	F	N	A	T	H	A	N
T	A	U	B	D	V	W	D	T	F
A	I	J	K	A	I	E	P	H	L
N	A	O	Z	A	D	O	K	A	J
O	H	E	X	L	Q	K	P	R	Z
J	Y	D	E	T	N	I	O	N	A

ABIATHAR

NATHAN

ZADOK

DAVID

SOLOMON

JONATHAN

BATHSHEBA

ANOINTED

BENAIAH

Rearrange the words to find different kinds of oil:

GKONIOC

RTOSAC

EIGNEN

DERUC

NERDIFE

EOILV

All the words in this wordsearch are in 2 Kings chapter 11!

1   Who tried to kill all the royal family? (8) _____

2   Who was hidden as a baby
    to escape being killed? (5)_____

3   Who hid Joash? (9) _____

4   In what building was Joash hidden? (6) _____

5   How many years was he hidden for? (3) _____

6   What did Joash become when he was
    seven years old? (4) _____

7   What did Jehoiada put on Joash's head? (5) _____

8   What instrument were the
    people playing? (8) _____

E	P	F	M	A	I	V	O	T	J	W
D	X	F	B	T	G	D	X	D	H	Z
N	L	S	C	H	U	I	T	R	Q	I
E	G	J	O	A	S	H	E	G	H	J
W	P	E	K	L	V	O	L	S	V	E
V	E	H	V	I	D	Y	P	Q	U	H
M	R	O	F	A	I	V	M	A	W	K
A	O	S	P	H	T	B	E	X	J	S
S	C	H	K	E	R	Z	T	R	Y	K
S	T	E	P	M	U	R	T	C	S	I
F	A	B	M	S	L	C	R	O	W	N
Q	Y	A	X	B	N	O	L	Z	N	G

Joash was hidden in the Temple to escape being killed

When he was seven
he was made king

Read 2 Kings 22-25 and 2 Chronicles 34

How old was Josiah when he became king? ☐ years old (Look up 2 Kings 22:1)

Put these bits of the story in the right order:

Josiah reads it and is worried – the people haven't obeyed what is written in the book.	Hilkiah the priest finds the book of the Law while the Temple is being repaired.	Josiah reads it to the people and renews Israel's covenant with God.	Josiah decides to repair the Temple

NUMBER ☐   NUMBER ☐   NUMBER ☐   NUMBER ☐

What did Josiah promise to God when he renewed the covenant? **Cross out every other letter to find out** (the first two have been done for you).

Josiah ordered Hilkiah and the other priests to take the things dedicated to worshipping the stars and other gods out of the Temple so that all the people would go back to worshipping the One True God.

Read 2 Chronicles 2-4

Some of the workmen have lost their tools. **Can you find them?**
After that, you can help by colouring the temple.

Find these tools for the workmen

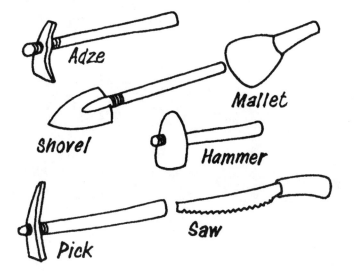

Adze

Mallet

Shovel

Hammer

Pick

Saw

Word search

T	U	F	R	A	D	E	C	A	N
S	R	B	Z	N	Y	M	E	C	E
F	E	Q	O	Y	A	T	Y	W	X
R	P	R	D	X	W	P	P	B	O
S	I	L	V	E	R	V	D	L	I
Z	N	R	L	E	M	D	C	U	D
C	U	S	S	G	O	L	J	E	H
N	J	S	E	Z	N	O	R	B	B
J	A	G	I	V	Q	G	K	P	U
B	K	P	U	R	P	L	E	L	H

GOLD
SILVER
BRONZE
IRON
RED
BLUE
PURPLE
CEDAR
CYPRESS
JUNIPER

Help the foreign workers find the temple

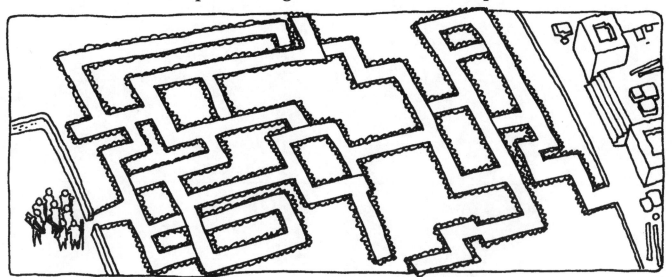

Read 2 Chronicles 14

Asa was a good king who did what God commanded. He had
an army of 300,000 men from the tribe of Judah, and 280,000
men from the tribe of Benjamin. All together, this made

$$\begin{array}{r} 280{,}000 \\ +\ 300{,}000 \\ \hline \textbf{men} \end{array}$$

Then the Egyptian army attacked them –
there were 1,000,000 soldiers in this army.
Which army would you expect to win?

Asa's army ☐   The Egypian army ☐

Asa was very worried. He knew that the
Egyptian army had many more soldiers
than he had. So he asked God for help in
this prayer:

What happened next?
**Read 2 Chronicles 14:12 – write the
words on the lines and draw it in
the space here:**

*Help us, O Lord our God.
We depend on you.
We fight against
this large army
in your name.
Lord, you are our God.
Don't let anyone win
against you.*

(2 Chronicles 14:11)

Why did Asa's army win the battle?
Colour in the dotted bits to find out why.

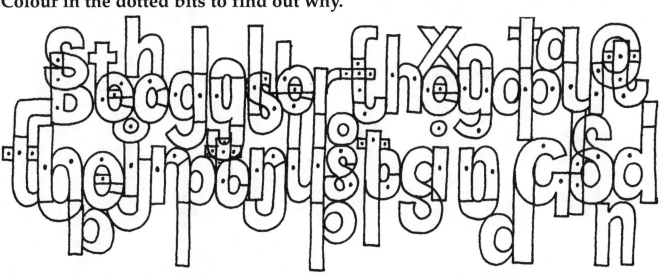

Read 2 Chronicles 26

Uzziah was king of Israel.
**Which of these things would he
have been able to do if he wanted?**

HAVE AN ENORMOUS BANQUET ☐

PUT SOMEONE TO DEATH ☐

TELL PEOPLE TO WORK FOR HIM ☐

ORDER HIS ARMY TO ATTACK
ANOTHER COUNTRY ☐

Unscramble the bold words to finish the story:

Uzziah had been very **huffalit** to God when he was younger,
but as he got more **vprelofu** he began to think that he could do
innhagty. One day, he went into the **pleemt** to burn incense,
a **obj** that only the priests were allowed to do. They **ldto** him not
to, but Uzziah just **dotshue** at them. Because of this, **oyserpl**
appeared on his skin as a punishment for doing what was wrong.

Uzziah's powerful position was given to him by God, but he thought it meant he
could do anything. In these situations, decide what would be God's way of doing
things, and cross out the thing that is wrong.

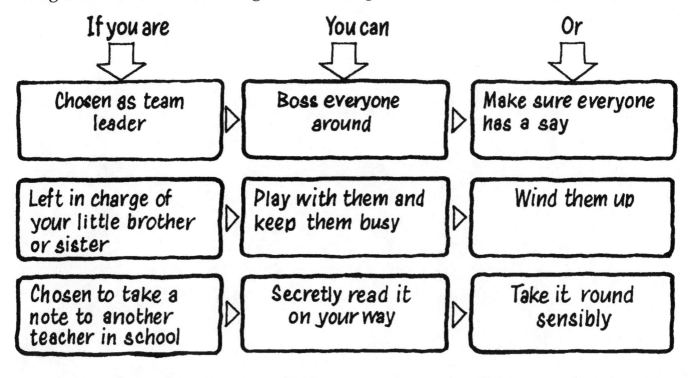

If you are	You can	Or
Chosen as team leader	Boss everyone around	Make sure everyone has a say
Left in charge of your little brother or sister	Play with them and keep them busy	Wind them up
Chosen to take a note to another teacher in school	Secretly read it on your way	Take it round sensibly

Read Isaiah 6

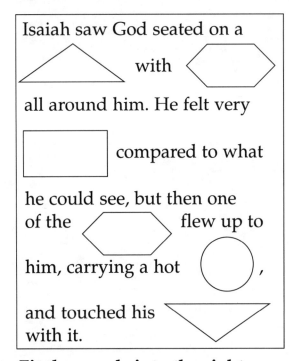

Isaiah saw God seated on a _____ with _____ all around him. He felt very _____ compared to what he could see, but then one of the _____ flew up to him, carrying a hot _____, and touched his _____ with it.

Fit the words into the right shapes in the story.

What did the angel with the coal say to Isaiah? **Join the dots to find out.**

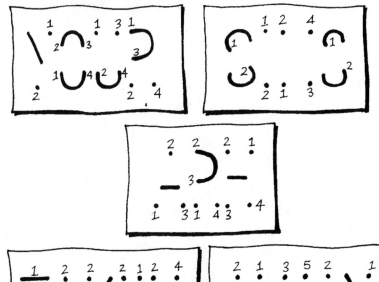

COAL   SINFUL   LIPS   THRONE   ANGELS

Here I am. Send me!

Isaiah had a vision of heaven while he was in the Temple. (Isaiah 6:8)
Draw a picture here of what you'd imagine heaven to be like.

HEAVEN

Read Jeremiah 29

When Nebuchadnezzar attacked Jerusalem, he took some of the people captive, and made them go to a far-off country called Babylon.

A B E I J L M N O R S U X Y

Jeremiah was in ⊕Þ≡⊥φ♂⊙Þ:

‒ ‒ ‒ ‒ ‒ ‒ ‒ ‒ ‒

and wrote to the Þ℅‡⊙Þφ

‒ ‒ ‒ ‒ ‒ ‒

who had been taken away to

□♂□⋈⊙✡Δ

‒ ‒ ‒ ‒ ‒ ‒ ‒

Draw pictures in the boxes of what Jeremiah told the people to do.

Plant gardens and eat what you grow in them

Build houses and settle down

Do you think the people wanted to come home quickly?   YES ☐   NO ☐

Do you think that Jeremiah thought it would only be a short time before they could go home?   YES ☐   NO ☐

After how many years would God bring the exiles home again?

6 x 5 + 40 = _____ years

(check in Jeremiah 29:10)

Marry and have children

Read Ezekiel 2 and 3

In a vision, God told the prophet Ezekiel that he needed him to speak to the people of Israel, who were turning against him. He said

'You must speak my words to them, whether they listen or fail to listen.' EZEKIEL 2:7

Put the page up to a mirror, or look at it from the back to see what it says.

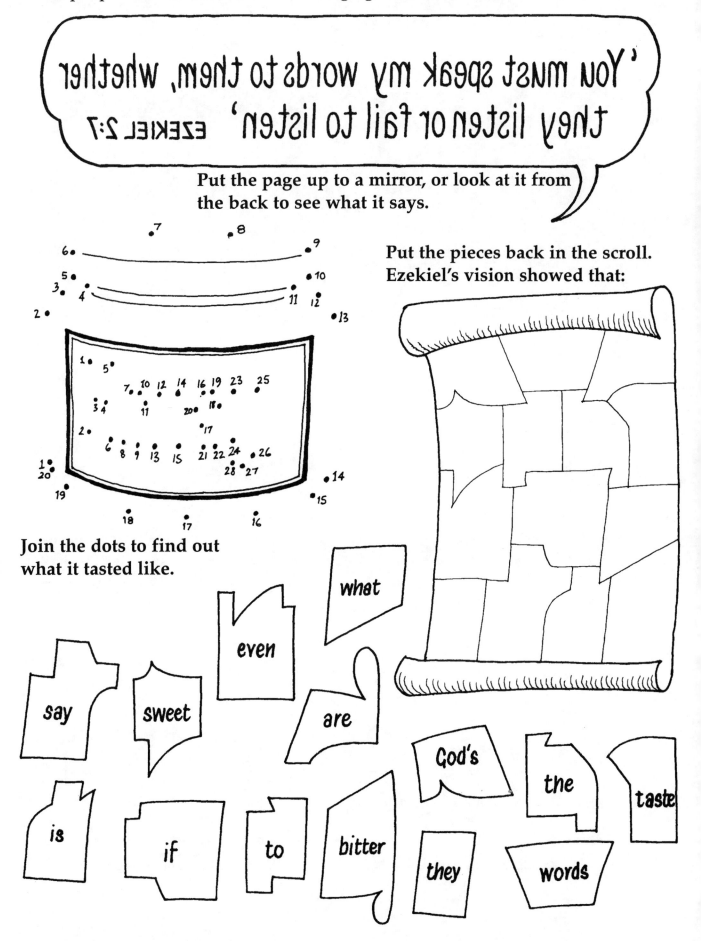

Put the pieces back in the scroll. Ezekiel's vision showed that:

Join the dots to find out what it tasted like.

what

even

say   sweet   are

is   if   to   bitter   God's   the   taste

they   words

Read Ezekiel 37:1-14

God gives us life

God puts us together

Word search

G	Z	I	E	X	P	U	D	B
R	K	H	G	I	H	T	A	S
J	E	Y	W	T	A	C	T	I
L	J	G	V	O	K	O	S	O
L	F	K	N	F	E	Q	I	D
U	F	A	R	I	H	N	R	E
K	O	L	B	X	F	C	W	N
S	O	S	Q	S	H	I	N	M
Y	T	B	H	V	M	G	R	P
R	U	C	Z	M	T	A	L	W

TOE
FOOT
SHIN
THIGH
FINGER
WRIST
ARM
BACK
SKULL

Find the bones

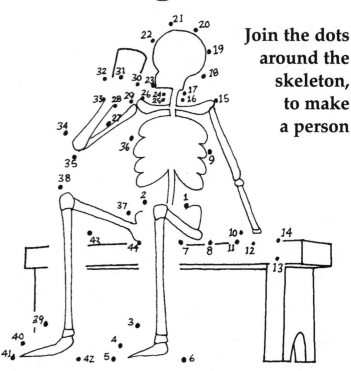

Join the dots
around the
skeleton,
to make
a person

God makes us real

Nebuchadnezzar's dream

Read Daniel 2

King Nebuchadnezzar asked his advisers and wise men to tell him what he had been dreaming and what it meant, but of course, none of them could do it. Except for Daniel.

Fill in the blanks using the words below to find out how he did it.

Daniel and his _ _ _ _ _ _ _
asked _ _ _ to show them
what the king's _ _ _ _ _ _
was about, and God _ _ _ _ _ _
him in a vision. Only God _ _ _ _ _
exactly what goes on _ _ _ _ _ _
someone's mind.

FRIENDS   SHOWED

KNOWS

DREAM   GOD

INSIDE

Look up Daniel 2:31-33 and draw what the king dreamed.

If you know what these people were dreaming last night, tick the box next to them.

You ☐

Your mum ☐

The Queen ☐

Your teacher ☐   The postman ☐

Which is the only dream you'd know without being told? _____

Read Amos 5:21-24

How many instruments can you see?

God likes music, but he
likes kindness more

How many bad things can you see?

How many good things can you see?

Let's worship God
and be kind as well!

Read Micah 4:1-4

Find the 6 hidden weapons

Beat swords into ploughs

Beating swords into ploughs would not be easy. Like the blacksmith's work, it would be:

> DRAH
> TOH
> SUOREGNAD
> LUFLIKS

Turn the words around.
Making peace can be like that too.

Crack the code to find out how God wants us to live.

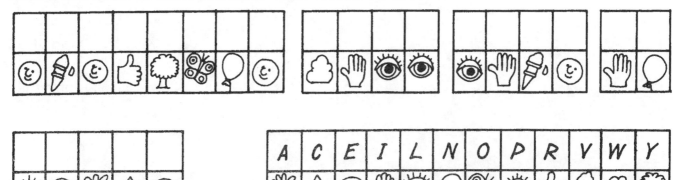

Read Matthew 18:1-5

**How many children in the crowd
around Jesus? (Some are hiding)**

Children are central

Bring the children into the centre of the church.

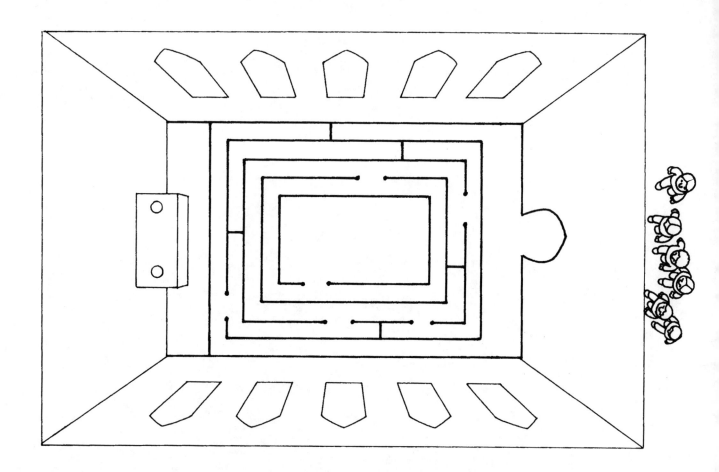

Read Matthew 26:26-29

Can you find ten differences between these pictures?

Jesus calls us to share

What can we share with our friends?
Unscramble the words and write them under the pictures.

DFOO ( ) NRDIK ( ) SYTO ( )

EITM ( ) MLSSIE ( ) RATSE ( )

Last Supper wordsearch

JESUS   SHARING
DISCIPLES   BREAD
WINE   BROKEN   SUPPER
KINGDOM   FORGIVENESS
OFFER

J	E	S	U	S	R	O	H	E	Q	S	X
T	F	I	V	D	S	A	D	B	J	S	R
K	S	H	A	R	U	A	M	G	R	E	K
S	J	C	B	F	P	N	H	L	F	N	O
H	Z	X	R	R	P	Y	V	F	M	E	R
A	C	F	O	R	E	G	O	X	D	V	M
R	E	A	K	L	R	A	I	U	A	I	F
I	P	T	E	N	I	S	D	Y	O	G	S
N	B	E	N	I	W	Q	K	G	B	R	W
G	E	K	I	N	G	D	O	M	P	O	U
F	U	R	G	I	V	R	Z	C	W	F	E
D	I	S	C	P	L	E	S	H	L	R	J

Read Matthew 26:36-46

Jesus is in
trouble.
He needs his
friends.
Where are they?

Don't be sleepy –
be a friend

Here are some lonely people. Unscramble the words to show where they are.

IN SNPIRO

IN SLHAOTPI

AT MEHO

**How can we be friends to lonely people?
Reverse the letters then find the words
on the grid.**

SREYARP	SGNITUO
SRETTEL	SDNARRE
STISIV	SYADHTRIB
ENOHPELET	SNOITATIVNI

```
I N V I T A T I O N S
C G E N O H P E L E T
E B I R T H D A Y S D
Q S P R A Y F D I M O
E R R A N D S C S R U
U E F N V D V R S I T
Z T O A H A E L S Y I
O T B E T Y H F Q D N
K E X K A S W P B J G
C L N R B V I S I T S
A R P I R T H D A X F
```

Read Matthew 27:33-44

Can you find a hammer, three nails, a cup of wine and a pair of dice hidden in the picture?

God gets hurt

Jesus suffered because

He was ELTNEG and the others were TNELOIV
He was ELBMUH and the others were DUORP
He was TSENOH and the others were TSENOHSID
(Turn the words round to solve the puzzle)

Many people today are hurt because they are gentle and others are violent. Sometimes they decorate crosses with pictures to show they trust Jesus.

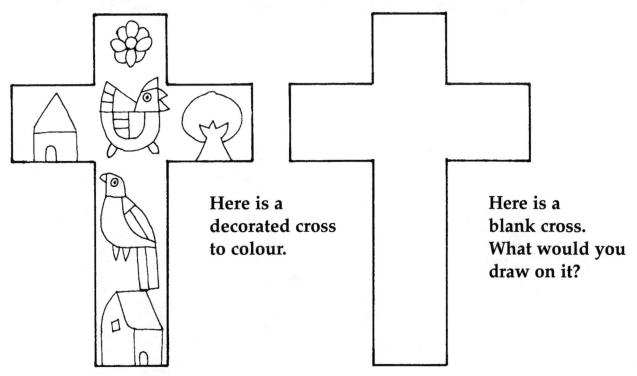

Here is a decorated cross to colour.

Here is a blank cross. What would you draw on it?

Read Matthew 28:1-10

**The six frightened soldiers are hiding.
Can you find them?**

God gives life

Help the women find the tomb.

Read Luke 1:5-25

Luke 1, verses 8-17

ACROSS

3 What was the angel's name?
5 What was Zechariah burning?
6 What was Zechariah's job?
7 Which prophet would
   Zechariah's son be like?

DOWN

1 What would Zechariah's
   son be filled with?
2 What would Zechariah's
   son not be allowed to drink?
4 What appeared to
   Zechariah?

Rearrange the letters in the ☐ boxes to find out what Zechariah was told to call his son.

Read Luke 2:1-7

**Jesus was laid in a _____
because there was no _____ at the inn**

God wants a home

Many people are homeless. There is no room.
Help the homeless people find homes.

Read Luke 2:41-52

Can you find 10 differences?

Children should ask questions

Some questions are easy.
How many fingers?

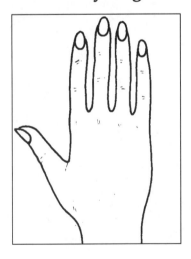

Some are harder.
Where is Timbuctoo?
What is Prince William's middle name?

Some are almost impossible.
How many stars in the sky?

**How many questions can you think of
starting with: How? What? Where? When? Who?
and best of all WHY?**

Read Luke 8:26-39

At the end of the story, what did Jesus tell the man to do? Unscramble the message by spelling the words back to front.

OT	LLET	LLA	EHT
_ _	_ _ _ _	_ _ _	_ _ _

NWOT	WOH	HCUM
_ _ _ _	_ _ _	_ _ _ _

SUSEJ	DAH	ENOD
_ _ _ _ _	_ _ _	_ _ _ _

ROF	MIH
_ _ _	_ _ _

The wild man in the desert

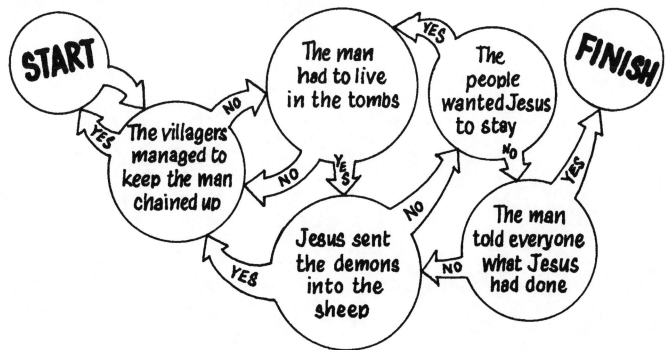

START → The villagers managed to keep the man chained up

YES / NO → The man had to live in the tombs

NO / YES → Jesus sent the demons into the sheep

YES → The people wanted Jesus to stay

NO → The man told everyone what Jesus had done

YES → FINISH

Read Luke 15:11-32

The son was greedy
and wasted his father's goodness.
We also get greedy
and waste God's goodness.

Find these words on the grid.

AIR TREES WATER WASTE POLLUTION
BOTTLES CANS PAPER RECYCLING CFC

```
P O L L U T I O N A E J
W A T E H P V D Y W H C
C L U O V O T K C A L E
S N A C G Z B S Y S D C
F X B J W H N N E T I A
B O T T L E S B S E E R
A R G N I L C Y C E R M
R P O L L U Y F W M R T
E I P E R A A M T E F T
T K R E C I C L P Q U O
A C S G Q R X A Z D L B
W A C F C R P A P R S T
```

The journey home

What must the lost son go through to get home?

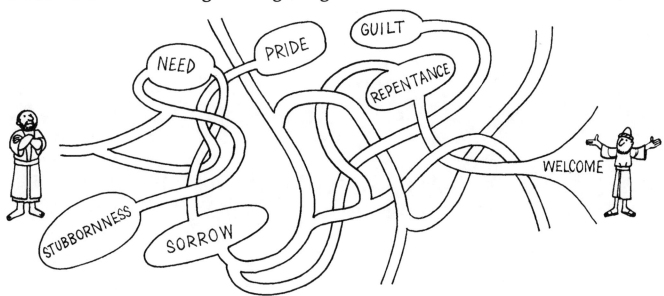

NEED PRIDE GUILT REPENTANCE WELCOME STUBBORNNESS SORROW

**Why is the elder brother
left out of the party?**

Reverse the words.

Because of:

EDIRP   REGNA
YSUOLAEJ   ECILAM
And most of all:
FLESMIH

Read Luke 19:1-10

Find Zaccaeus by colouring the dotted shapes

What would you give Jesus to eat? Colour your favourite foods

Jesus is everybody's friend

Crack the code and complete the sentences

A C D E F G H I N O R S T X

Zaccaeus collected

Zaccaeus was a

Zaccaeus was

Zaccaeus was

Zaccaeus was by meeting Jesus

Sharing showed friendship

Being Jesus' helped Zaccaeus become honest

Why are these people looking grumpy? Look up Luke 19:7

Read Luke 24:13-35

**Help the two disciples find their
way from Jerusalem to Emmaus**

**Cross off the wrong words
in the boxes to make the story right**

It was ⬚ 3/17 days since Jesus had died,
and two of the disciples were going
to ⬚ Jerusalem/Emmaus . Jesus
apppeared to them, but they
⬚ hardly/did not recognise him.
    Jesus told them how the
⬚ prophets/angels in the Old Testament
had said about what was going to
happen to him.
    The ⬚ disciples/shepherds invited
him in to their house, and they
recognised him when he broke the
⬚ chair/bread . Then they knew
that Jesus really was alive.

Read John 2:1-11   **Can you guess who has water and who has wine?**

Jesus turns water into wine

Word Search

Find the words in the grid, and put them in the correct list

God likes to be

_____

_____

_____

_____

_____

H	A	P	P	Y	O	B	T	L	B
O	D	X	B	L	E	H	W	R	A
P	L	O	K	F	G	O	O	D	D
E	A	D	T	I	D	U	L	L	Z
F	H	J	R	H	A	R	E	N	G
U	Q	B	F	K	S	N	U	J	N
L	O	V	I	N	G	O	C	P	I
I	G	Y	U	I	P	G	Q	S	R
L	U	F	R	A	E	F	M	M	O
A	Y	L	E	N	O	L	V	C	B

God doesn't like to be

_____

_____

_____

_____

_____

HAPPY   BORING   GOOD
SAD   DULL   LOVING
FUN   BRIGHT   BAD
HOPEFUL FEARFUL   LONELY

Use a red crayon to turn the water into wine

Read John 4:1-10

Crack the code to complete the sentences

□ ◇ ⊙ ◖ ◗ ◺ ◿ ◹ ◺ ▽ ◁ ▽◺

A B DHIMNOP RT UY

Some people thought the woman was ◇ □ ⊙, and ⊙ ◗ ▷ ◁ ◺

Jesus knew she was ◖ ▽ ◺ □ ◺ and ◗ ◺ ▽ ◹ ▷ ◁ □ ◺ ◁

Well, Well, Well!

Help the woman find the well

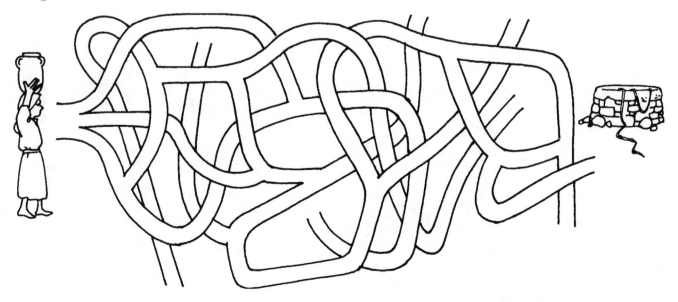

Read John 21:1-14

Some of Jesus' disciples spent all night fishing on the sea of Galilee, but by the morning they hadn't caught a thing.

Who did they see on the shore?_____(John 21:4)

What did he say to them?_____

_____

(John 21:6)

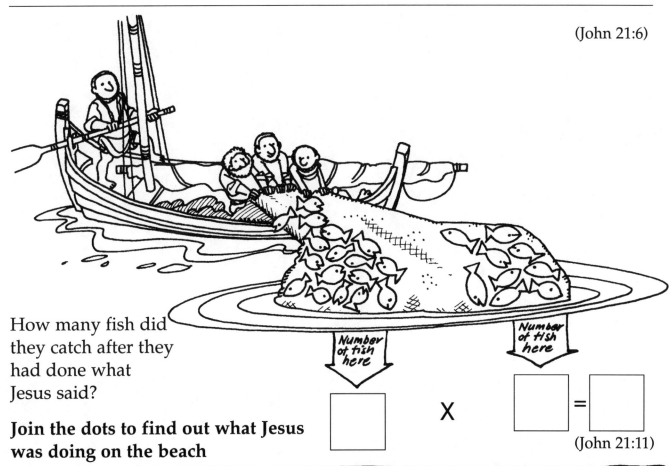

How many fish did they catch after they had done what Jesus said?

Number of fish here

Number of fish here

☐   X   ☐ = ☐

(John 21:11)

Join the dots to find out what Jesus was doing on the beach

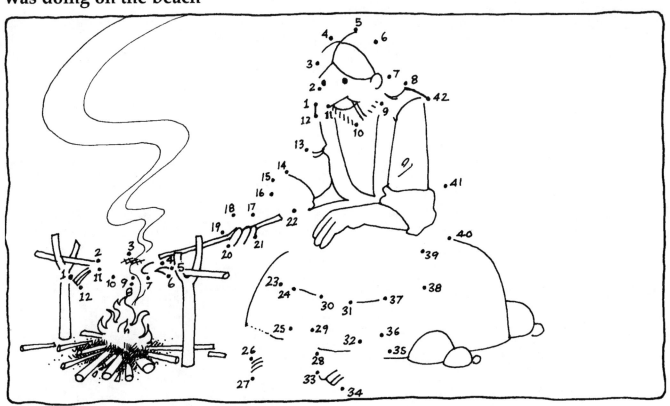

Read Acts 9:20-25, 2 Corinthians 11:32-33

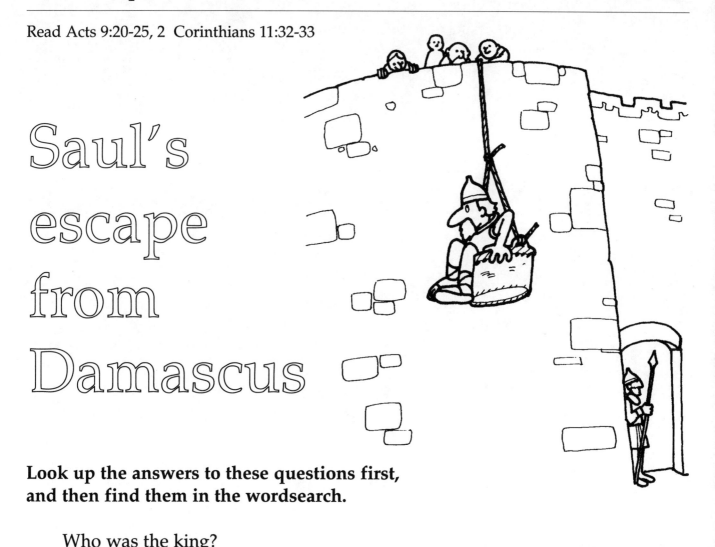

Saul's escape from Damascus

**Look up the answers to these questions first,
and then find them in the wordsearch.**

Who was the king?
(2 Corinthians 11:33) _ _ _ _ _ _

Where was Saul preaching that Jesus was the Son of God?
(Acts 9:20) _ _ _ _ _ _ _ _ _ _

Which city was he in?
(2 Corinthians 11:32) _ _ _ _ _ _ _ _

Where were the soldiers keeping watch
  to make sure Saul didn't escape?
(Acts 9:24) _ _ _ _ _ _ _ _ _

What did he escape in?
(Acts 9:25) _ _ _ _ _ _

When did this happen?
(Acts 9:25) _ _ _ _ _

```
R Q B S A O P C F H Z P
W I N E Q T E U S N I S
H R E U C P H N I G H T
D P C G D T K M S G E J
V T Y O S A P E A K N E
M L O G Y R M P S D E K
X T E A B E C A H F A M
I T L N J T B L S O S R
C I T Y G A T E S C P L
S F G S V S B H C L U R
D P A M Y A W Q I D W S
```

Read Acts 12:6-11

Help the angel to find Peter

God sets people free

What must we be freed from?
Unscramble the words
in the planks securing the
door and then find them in
the wordsearch.

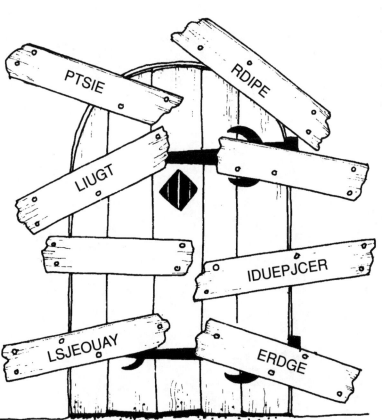

PTSIE

RDIPE

LIUGT

IDUEPJCER

LSJEQUAY

ERDGE

J	E	A	L	O	U	S	Y	A	R
M	T	Y	U	T	Q	Z	I	U	G
R	I	Z	N	W	Y	O	A	D	R
J	P	R	I	D	P	N	Y	X	E
D	S	A	C	R	T	D	O	A	E
G	O	N	I	E	L	R	E	E	D
X	I	D	Y	B	I	X	G	I	L
F	E	C	I	D	U	J	E	R	P
P	R	E	J	U	G	M	S	O	Z
G	U	I	L	X	K	C	R	H	P

Can you think of any more?
Write them on the planks.

Read Acts 19:23-41

Put these things in order of how expensive you think they are

BOOK   CAN OF SOUP   SILVER NECKLACE   WOODEN BRACELET   PAPER BAG   HAMSTER

1 _____

2 _____

3 _____

4 _____

5 _____

6 _____

If you wanted to make people think that something was really special and important, what would you make it out of?

WOOD ☐   GOLD OR SILVER ☐
PAPER ☐   CLAY ☐   PLASTIC ☐

What was Paul saying that made people not want to buy the idols? **Fill in his speech bubble.**

(Look up Acts 19:26 . . . the second part of the verse)

The craftsmen were angry that Paul had convinced people not to buy the idols, and they started a riot.

Read Acts 19:36-41 to find out what happened after this!

Read Acts 20:7-12

Count two letters on from the coded word to find the name of the person in this story (the first letter has been done already)

C S R W A F S Q

E _ _ _ _ _ _ _

or look up Acts 20:9!

Help Paul find his way down the steps.

START

FINISH

Cross out the X's to find what Paul said when he saw the young man:

DXOXNTBXEXAXLXAXR
XMXEXDXHXEXSXAXL
XIXVXEX

What happened when the young man fell asleep? (Acts 20:9).
Draw a picture here.

_ _ _ _ _   _ _   _ _ _ _ _ _ _ _ _   _ _ _   _ _ _ _!

Read 1 Corinthians 10:17

Many grains of wheat

One loaf

Many people

One church

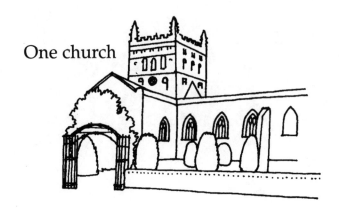

Many of One,
One of Many

Turn round the words in brackets

Many (SEGAP)   one (KOOB)
Many (SKCIRB) one (LLAW)
Many (SDROW)   one (NOMRES)

Join the dots to find what we share at Communion

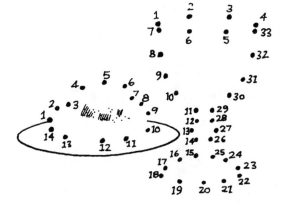

How many beads on the necklace?

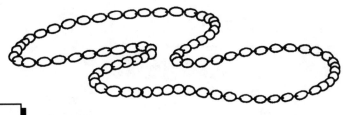

 Answer

Read 1 Corinthians 12:12-31

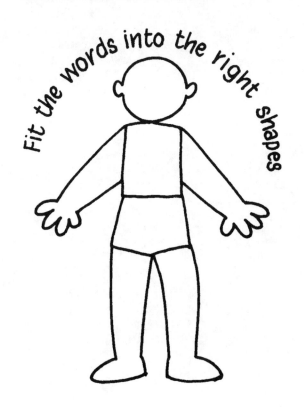

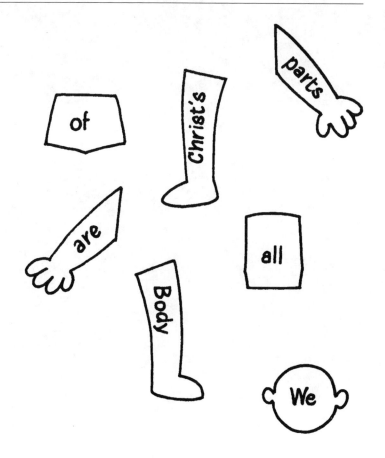

Fit the words into the right shapes

of　Christ's　parts　are　Body　all　We

Circle the ways that people can be useful to God

MAKING CUPS OF TEA

BEING A MISSIONARY

SINGING A SOLO IN CHURCH

PRAYING

BEING FRIENDLY TO A VISITOR TO CHURCH

DUSTING

DRAWING A PICTURE

PREACHING A SERMON

GIVING YOUR MUM OR DAD A HUG

(Look at this message in the mirror to find the answer!)

They're all useful to God!

So, jobs that don't look very important
to us are all important to God.

Read Galatians 5

Fit the words into the grid

3 Letters
JOY

4 Letters
LOVE

5 Letters
PEACE

8 Letters
KINDNESS
PATIENCE
GOODNESS

10 Letters
GENTLENESS

11 Letters
SELF-CONTROL

12 Letters
FAITHFULNESS

Live by the Spirit   Galatians 5:16

You can be a Christian just by following rules

You need the Holy Spirit to be able to live God's way

FALSE

You can live God's way all by yourself

TRUE

FALSE

TRUE

You still have to try hard if you want to follow Jesus

Read 1 Peter 2:4-12

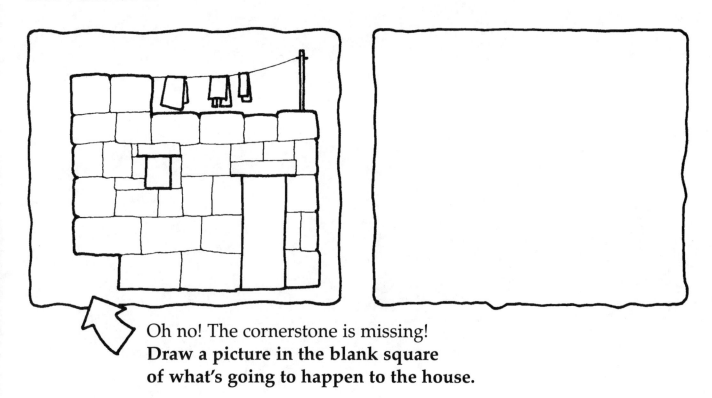

Oh no! The cornerstone is missing!
**Draw a picture in the blank square
of what's going to happen to the house.**

Here is something that
the prophet Isaiah wrote.
**Who do you think he is
talking about?**

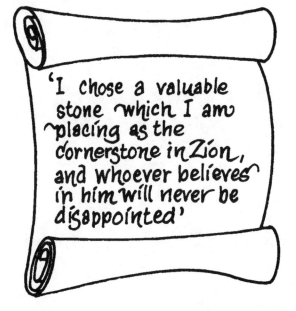

'I chose a valuable
stone which I am
placing as the
cornerstone in Zion,
and whoever believes
in him will never be
disappointed'

**Fill in the dotted shapes to find out
what God wants us to be like.**

Fit the right words into the spaces.

God wants us to _____ our _____ on Jesus

as he is the _____ (the most _____ stone)

and he won't let us down.   CORNERSTONE   BUILD   IMPORTANT   LIVES